North London

Edited By Catherine Cook

First published in Great Britain in 2019 by:

Young Writers
Remus House
Coltsfoot Drive
Peterborough
PE2 9BF
Telephone: 01733 890066
Website: www.youngwriters.co.uk

All Rights Reserved
Book Design by Spencer Hart
© Copyright Contributors 2019
Softback ISBN 978-1-78988-865-2
Hardback ISBN 978-1-83928-331-4
Printed and bound in the UK by BookPrintingUK
Website: www.bookprintinguk.com
YB0417WZ

Foreword

Dear Reader,

Are you ready to explore the wonderful delights of poetry?

Young Writers' *Poetry Patrol* gang set out to encourage and ignite the imaginations of 5-7 year-olds as they took their first steps into the magical world of poetry. With **Riddling Rabbit**, **Acrostic Croc** and **Sensory Skunk** on hand to help, children were invited to write an acrostic, sense poem or riddle on any theme, from people to places, animals to objects, food to seasons. *Poetry Patrol* is also a great way to introduce children to the use of poetic expression, including onomatopoeia and similes, repetition and metaphors, acting as stepping stones for their future poetic journey.

All of us here at Young Writers believe in the importance of inspiring young children to produce creative writing, including poetry, and we feel that seeing their own poem in print will keep that creative spirit burning brightly and proudly.

We hope you enjoy reading this wonderful collection as much as we enjoyed reading all the entries.

Contents

Bnos Beis Yaakov Primary School, Kingsbury Green

Noa Sobel (7)	1
Mimi Rottenberg (6)	2
Rosa Hoch (7)	3
Kayla Goldberg (7)	4
Sara Stopnitzky (7)	5
Odi Gertner (7)	6

Christ Church Brondesbury CE Primary School, London

Eron Ashani (6)	7
Ope Banjo (5)	8
Shai Higgins (5)	9
Labiba Khanum (6)	10
Ayaah Hafiz Gill (6)	11

Hazelwood Schools, Palmers Green

Jackson Grove (6)	12
Reuben Louis Ash (7)	13
Iris Burton (7)	14
Kanyiti-Laurat Issaka Sannie (6)	15
Yasmin Turker (7)	16
Lora Peycheva (7)	17
Elis-Elenor Angelova (7)	18
Tamerlan Mehmet (6)	19
Finn McKendry (6)	20
Chloe Sulaj (7)	21
Lucinda Lewtas (7)	22
Nat Buckley (7)	23
Valentina Pandelis (7)	24
Firdaous Bilaloglu (6)	25
David Bajraku (6)	26
Lily Hall (6)	27
Joseph Cooper (7)	28
Filippo Di Primio (6)	29
Sasha Barrett (7)	30
Pascal Speck Sheehan (7)	31
Lena Lambrou (5)	32
Amro Bawady (7)	33
Zoe Georgiou (6)	34
Andrei-Razvan Bandea (6)	35
Lena Altuncevahir	36
Aman Sunil Patel (6)	37
Nina Lis (6)	38
Kane Mahmoud (7)	39
Sofia Visheva (6)	40
Alana Scarlett Lambrou (7)	41
Jack Bufton (5)	42
Nell Naughton (6)	43
Matthew Kalemi (7)	44
Luca Antoniades (6)	45
Wiktor Swietochowski (6)	46
Aashna Pankhania (6)	47
Emma Serafinova-Noel (6)	48
Marawan Elawadi (6)	49
Alex Rawlinson (6)	50
Joe Robertson (7)	51
Edgar Loustalan (6)	52
Emma Sales (7)	53
Balazs Csanadi (7)	54
Stella Frangou (6)	55
Arabella Procter (5)	56
Sachin Verma (6)	57
Indie Houghton (6)	58
Alisa Yushchuk (6)	59
Panagiotis Tselios (7)	60

Selen Eyyub (6)	61
Kevin Hukalowicz (6)	62
Alessio Vento-Joyce (7)	63
Rosie Thwaites (6)	64
Lucas Morris (7)	65
Ben Gibbard (6)	66
Ahmet Tuncel (7)	67
Spyros Gkezos (7)	68
Rosa Beana Watson (7)	69
Barney Hailstone (6)	70
Alexander Philippos Costa Enright (6)	71
Sophia Velez Moncada (7)	72
Angelo Odunoye (6)	73
Chloe Philipou (6)	74
Ilirdi Bregu (6)	75
Jessica Kyriacou (7)	76
Lillian Ewan (6)	77
Leah Andrews (5)	78
Emma Kyriacou (7)	79
Autumn Wallis Ackroyd (7)	80
Arthur Gatland (6)	81
Annabelle El Issa (6)	82
Uthmaan Khairul (6)	83
Aynur Kara (7)	84
Maya Feier (6)	85
Sara Xhafa (6)	86
Pandora Paola Dimou (6)	87
Aaron Andrews (7)	88
Sylvie Chambers (6)	89
Aryaan Hussain (5)	90
Zayah Szabo Alexander (5)	91
Skyla Deegan (6)	92
Astrid Mosquera (6)	93

Kingsbury Green Primary School, Kingsbury

Levi Avram (6)	94
Manit Prashant Patel (7)	95
Ahmed Omran Istanakzai (7)	96
Rochelle Minara Wimalasuriya (7)	97
Dhruv Sompura (6)	98

Gino Brian (7)	99
Ayaan Chaudhary (7)	100
Elizabeth Triboi (6)	101
Zainab Bader (6)	102
Mikael Alderton (6)	103
David Boca (7)	104
Hussain Ali-Mostafa (7)	105
Eduard Reut (7)	106
Dihen Fernando (6)	107
Preesha Rabadia (6)	108

St Luke's CE School, London

Laith Alexander Brookman-Amissah (7)	109
Zoey Hoffmann (5)	110
Abigail Hoffmann (7)	111
Pardis Ashouri (7)	112
Chara Bewsher (6)	113
Aidegueosa Eliana Adun (6)	114
Partow Ashouri (7)	115
Haruna Miura (5)	116
Tamia Burrell (6)	117
Mikey Chatterton (7)	118
Marcus Meduri (6)	119
Zeinab Haider (7)	120
Isambard Geers (6)	121
Sofia Phillips (6)	122
Elle Jay Marshall (7)	123
Olivia McKenzie (6)	124
Claudia Kordys (7)	125
Rachel Blach de Faoite (6) & Lara	126
Rose Orly Raftery (5)	127
Matian Bllaca (7)	128
Georgina Gross (6)	129
Aaron Predko (6)	130
Beck Talanbek (5)	131
Michael Kudi Mafuamba (6)	132

St Mark's CE Primary School, Islington

Dara Olowoporoku (7)	133

Savannah Emily de Barry (7)	134
Malik Adam (7)	135
Nomqhele Zoleka Khumalo (7)	136
Romola Hume-Wright (6)	137
Cerys Rose Miller (6)	138
Rayanne Kasongo (7)	139
Kamran Salik (7)	140
Jacob Sipiano (6)	141
Deniz Dogan (7)	142
Jeriel Annan (5)	143
Pelumi Olujinmi (6)	144
Zackariah Ashik-O'Toole (6)	145
Joshua Falanka (6)	146
Jianing Guo (6)	147
Bayleigh Sweeney (6)	148
Asa Morphet (6)	149
Maisarah Miah (7)	150
Xanti Leizaola (6)	151
Ava Cunningham (6)	152
Jimmy Pipinka (6)	153
Nylah Dirosa-Brown (6)	154
Christian Solarin (6)	155
Rufus Morrell (6)	156
Dimitris Zamenopoulos (7)	157
Ethan Matthews-Appleby (6)	158
Daniel Adkin (6)	159
J'Quan Jackman (6)	160
Arjol William Xhihaj (6)	161
Sadie Taitt (6)	162

The Poems

Senses

I smell the buttercups in the spring
as I listen to the birds sing.
I taste my mummy's delicious cake,
In the warm summer sun.
I see the orange, green and red leaves
as I crunch in the autumn fun.
I feel the snowflakes in winter,
cold on my hands.

Noa Sobel (7)
Bnos Beis Yaakov Primary School, Kingsbury Green

I Wish I Was A Unicorn

I wish I was a unicorn.
I wish I was a unicorn because I would be pink
And have some silk.
I would have a horn
And everyone would sing.
I would be different from others.
I guess it's better to be like others.

Mimi Rottenberg (6)
Bnos Beis Yaakov Primary School, Kingsbury Green

Weather

Summer sun shines,
Autumn leaves fall,
Spring brings warm weather,
Winter is freezing cold.
All these types of weather,
God made it amazing.
Thank you, God, for all the seasons,
Summer, autumn, winter and spring.

Rosa Hoch (7)
Bnos Beis Yaakov Primary School, Kingsbury Green

My Life

When I'm bored,
I colour on the whiteboard.
When I drive my car,
I go very far.
When it was the spring,
I bought a new ring.
I like saying riddles,
When people get the giggles.

Kayla Goldberg (7)
Bnos Beis Yaakov Primary School, Kingsbury Green

I Can Fly

I can fly so very high.
I can fly and touch the sky.
I can fly, can you?
I can fly and make a stew.
I can fly, it's fun for everyone.
I can fly and send a letter.

Sara Stopnitzky (7)
Bnos Beis Yaakov Primary School, Kingsbury Green

Summer

Summer is hot.
Summer is nice and fun.
Summer is cool.
Summer is when we have ice cream.
Summer is when we go in the pool.
Summer is fun.

Odi Gertner (7)
Bnos Beis Yaakov Primary School, Kingsbury Green

The Dangerous Jungle Animal

I live in the watery jungle.
I am a reptile so I am cold-blooded.
I have smooth scales.
I can smell with my tongue.
I am as silent as a ghost.
I slither on my tummy.
What am I?

Answer: A snake.

Eron Ashani (6)
Christ Church Brondesbury CE Primary School, London

What Am I?

I live in the ground
I am a mammal
I have fun
I have jagged claws
I have six fine fingers
I like to eat gold carrots
I can jump high.
What am I?

Answer: A rabbit.

Ope Banjo (5)
Christ Church Brondesbury CE Primary School, London

The Roaring Poem

I live in a deep jungle.
I am a mammal so I am warm-blooded.
I can run faster than a cheetah.
I have yellow and brown skin, as light as a feather.
I love to eat leaves.
What am I?

Shai Higgins (5)
Christ Church Brondesbury CE Primary School, London

A Flying Poem

I live on a tropical island.
I am a bird.
I have warm blood and fluffy feathers.
I can fly so high.
I also lay little eggs.
I fly as slow as a snail.
What am I?

Labiba Khanum (6)
Christ Church Brondesbury CE Primary School, London

Crunchy Carrots

I live on the bright green grass.
I am a mammal.
I have big ears that are as white as snow.
I can jump so high.
What am I?

Answer: A rabbit.

Ayaah Hafiz Gill (6)
Christ Church Brondesbury CE Primary School, London

A Good Friend

F inding a good friend is wonderful.
R espect is important to being a good friend.
I nstead of always doing what you want,
E veryone should be happy.
N ever be mean to your friend.
D ancing together is fun.
S leepovers, midnight feasts and whispering.
H olidays, happy feelings and building sandcastles in the sun.
I love kicking a ball around with my friends.
P laying games, cosy and warm in winter.

Jackson Grove (6)
Hazelwood Schools, Palmers Green

Football Stadium: Emirates

E ating the divine hot dogs at halftime.
M y heart beating fast like a Bugatti.
I n the stadium, the excited people cheer.
R ed shirts flash across the pitch like flying reindeer.
A rsenal's home, the pride of North London.
T urnstiles creak and control the crowds.
E xciting football makes everyone joyful.
S ome might say that the Emirates Stadium is the best in England, but I think it's the best in the world.

Reuben Louis Ash (7)
Hazelwood Schools, Palmers Green

Dreams

D reams can be about anything you want them to be. They could be about magic, wonder or scary, ferocious monsters.
R ight over the rainbow, puppies yap and pretty, soft and gentle bluebirds fly.
E nchanting, powerful dragons flap their huge, colourful wings in the sky full of fluffy white clouds.
A ll the fluffy, kind animals over the rainbow play and draw all day.
M agic always fills the air.
S uper cool stars glow in the night sky.

Iris Burton (7)
Hazelwood Schools, Palmers Green

Unicorns

U niquely beautiful and majestically, friendly animals.
N ature's true reflection of balance and harmony.
I nfectiously touching all hearts with imaginations.
C olours ooze out of their horns.
O verjoyed kids but adults see no myth.
R evealing the soft part of the wild, inspiring innovative stories.
N o one avoids the beauty of their glorious grey wings.
S uper sweet, sensory, sensational animals. Unicorns!

Kanyiti-Laurat Issaka Sannie (6)
Hazelwood Schools, Palmers Green

Big Dreams

D reams are about imagination, what flows in the mind.

"**R** efulgent realm," said the lady. "What a wonderful day."

E legantly, she trod like a Welsh Corgi. *Boom, clang!*

A fter the cacophony, she heard a meowing cat.

M ysteriously, there was also a bunny.

S uddenly, the bunny and cat smelt her hand. They are now friends and that is the power of imagination.

Yasmin Turker (7)
Hazelwood Schools, Palmers Green

Ice Skate

I ce skating is as cold as winter.
C ools you when you are feeling hot.
E xciting new lessons to learn.

S kating is hard at first but then you get used to it.
K een to return again.
A ctions are hard when you are a child.
T itanic ice rink.
I t's fun ice skating.
N ice ice skating teachers.
G lamorous ice skating floor.

Lora Peycheva (7)
Hazelwood Schools, Palmers Green

My School

Today my dear school
For you I wrote this poem

Spring and summer, autumn and winter
All the children grow up with love
And their dreams. Hazelwood School
You are our oasis in the desert
Thank you of course for the
Happiness to learn here

You teach me to stand and go ahead
Show initiative and courage
You are my beloved school
You are my wonderful world!

Elis-Elenor Angelova (7)
Hazelwood Schools, Palmers Green

My Mum

My mum linked my life
From her love and care thread.
My mum linked my life
And gave me a kiss on my head.
My mum linked my life
From her prayers and sleepless nights.
My mum linked my life
And her threads for me were like lights.
My mum linked my life
To present me the whole Earth.
Where does she take the thread?
To link my life as she secretly undoes hers.

Tamerlan Mehmet (6)
Hazelwood Schools, Palmers Green

Baby Lizard

B aby lizard went to the jungle.
A big snake slithered around it.
B aby lizard started to run.
Y ummy food, thought the snake.

L ittle baby ran away.
I t tackled the snake's
Z ig-zaggy tail.
A ll of the snakes tried to get it.
R un, baby lizard, run!
D addy was waiting for the baby lizard.

Finn McKendry (6)
Hazelwood Schools, Palmers Green

Gymnastics

G irls and boys will participate.
Y ou will see all sorts of activities.
M onkey bars are by far the best.
N ever a day without having fun.
A lways keeping fit.
S howing off your skills.
T eachers challenge us.
I love gymnastics.
C hampions win the gold medal.
S hine bright when you perform.

Chloe Sulaj (7)
Hazelwood Schools, Palmers Green

Dreams

D reams are some imaginative things, you can dream of anything even unicorns.
R iding gigantic elephants in India and watching the beautiful, pretty dances.
E xciting adventures in the clouds with alicorns and birds.
A mazing, cuddly and cute rainbow sausage dogs jump over the rainbow.
M agical forests with unicorns, fairies, bunnies and pixies.

Lucinda Lewtas (7)
Hazelwood Schools, Palmers Green

The End Of The Season

F un, exciting and tense sport.
O h my, what a goal!
O h, what a view!
T ottenham, Christian Eriksen dashing rapidly down the wing.
B lows it into the Arsenal box.
A rsenal defenders helplessly jumping.
L ucas Moura gets in front of Mustafi
L ucas Moura volley scissor-kick: top corner, 3-2! Who's in fourth?

Nat Buckley (7)
Hazelwood Schools, Palmers Green

Beautiful, Lovely And Special Summer

Summer sounds like ocean waves waving in the sea.
Summer tastes like salty, green, slimy seaweed.
Summer feels like a big, sweaty, hot forehead.
Summer sounds like joyful, lovely children happily playing.
Summer smells like sweet, tasty and delicious ice creams.
Summer looks like kind birds singing a beautiful song in the trees.
Summer is as hot as the sun.

Valentina Pandelis (7)
Hazelwood Schools, Palmers Green

Zebras

Z ooming briskly around in their protective herds.
E xcitedly searching for some tantalisingly tasty grass to eat.
B lack and white stripes baffling their prey.
R apidly running as fast as a ferocious leopard.
A frica's jungle is their spacious and colourful habitat.
S eeing them is like a confusing optical illusion.

Firdaous Bilaloglu (6)
Hazelwood Schools, Palmers Green

Footballer Called David

Here comes the ref!
I put on my boots and head for the ball,
I race and I run, I hope not to fall!
I aim for the goal and for the net
I'm ready to score, it's not easy yet.
In fact, it's quite hard,
To keep my temper and avoid the red card.
Next game, I intend to please the crowd,
To make my team happy and my mum proud.

David Bajraku (6)
Hazelwood Schools, Palmers Green

The Swimming Lesson

S plashing with kicking legs.
W ater-filled pool, a lovely blue colour.
I love diving really deep.
M y goggles are bright pink.
M ummy sits, watching through the glass.
I am listening to my teacher.
N early home time, we all jump in the pool.
G oing swimming is really cool.

Lily Hall (6)
Hazelwood Schools, Palmers Green

It's Good To Be Fair

F ractions are great, tricky and fun.
A ddition is brilliant.
I like maths.
R eady to start maths.
N ow it's maths time.
E nfield schools really like maths,
S ome maths is really tricky, hard and challenging.
S ome maths is so easy you can do eight sums in ten seconds.

Joseph Cooper (7)
Hazelwood Schools, Palmers Green

Ronaldo

R onaldo's team won a hundred and forty-seven times.
O n the weekend, they play the matches
N obody plays the match during the week
A mazing kicks
L ucky they have Ronaldo, so it's good again.
D ays and days they practise
O h wow, he scored more than a hundred goals.

Filippo Di Primio (6)
Hazelwood Schools, Palmers Green

Grandma, Grandma, Where Is My Treat?

Grandma, grandma, where is my wonderful treat for me to eat?
Look up, look down, look round and round.
No clue.
Is it blue?
Did it fly away today?
No clue.
Did the strong wind blow it up in a china cup?
Is it up in space, where the round moon has a face?
No clue.
Wow, somebody found it. Thank you!

Sasha Barrett (7)
Hazelwood Schools, Palmers Green

Pickford

P enalties are hard to save.
I ncredible saves are what I do best.
C atching curves coming out of nowhere.
K icking the football upfield.
F orever saving shots.
O rangutan arms help save penalties.
R icharlison plays on my football team.
D iving to stop goals.

Pascal Speck Sheehan (7)
Hazelwood Schools, Palmers Green

Only I Believe

U nicorns are magical.
N o one can find their enchanted forest.
I maginary some believe, not me!
C areful, don't scare them away.
O nly a glimmer shimmers in the distance.
R esting gracefully
N uzzling their beautiful horns
S pellbinding loveliness.

Lena Lambrou (5)
Hazelwood Schools, Palmers Green

Spring

Spring is as colourful as a rainbow.
Spring is the best weather,
everyone loves spring.
Spring, spring, spring, spring.
Spring has lots of flowers
like daffodils, daisies, tulips and roses.
We like playing in the spring.
We go to different places
like the London Eye, Big Ben
and the Tower of London.

Amro Bawady (7)
Hazelwood Schools, Palmers Green

Summer Shine

S un is shining bright, we are covered in light.
U mbrellas away.
M eeting my friends, dressed in our summer clothes.
M mm, eating ice cream is delicious!
E ating, dancing and playing away on this summer's day!
R unning out to play in the sun is such fun.

Zoe Georgiou (6)
Hazelwood Schools, Palmers Green

Romania

R omania is my favourite country.
O nly when I go on holiday I meet
M any friends and play games with the ball
A nd have so many animals: cats, dogs
N othing compares to meet with my grandmother, she
I s special to me
A nd I love her very much.

Andrei-Razvan Bandea (6)
Hazelwood Schools, Palmers Green

Summer

S unny days make us full of joy.
U se sunglasses and a cap on hot days
M ake a sandcastle at the beach.
M aybe bigger than your room!
E at ice cream like the colour of the rainbow.
R emember your ice cream can melt before you finish it on a hot sunny day.

Lena Altuncevahir
Hazelwood Schools, Palmers Green

My Favourite Holidays

H otels in Spain are fun.
O ceans are deep with shades of blue and green.
L aughing at Goofy in Disney World.
I eat different types of ice cream.
D oing lots of swimming in Sri Lanka.
A mazing eels in the aquarium.
Y ummy breakfast in hotels.

Aman Sunil Patel (6)
Hazelwood Schools, Palmers Green

Buddy And His Fun Days

There's a dog called Buddy,
That loves everybody,
His farts are smelly,
He rolls onto his belly.
He likes to play with his ball,
And he likes to roll.
When the doors open, he's crazy
But normally he's quite lazy.
He loves to have fun
And he loves to lie down in the sun.

Nina Lis (6)
Hazelwood Schools, Palmers Green

What Am I?

I am found in deep, murky water.
I have scales on my body.
I am a reptile.
I have a powerful jaw to crush my prey.
I like to eat juicy meat.
I have sharp teeth.
I have a strong tail.
I have sharp claws and spikes on my tail.
What am I?

Answer: A crocodile.

Kane Mahmoud (7)
Hazelwood Schools, Palmers Green

Fruits Acrostic Poem

F ruits and vegetables are healthy foods to eat.
R unning is healthy for your body too.
U sually, we eat five to ten servings of fruits and vegetables a day.
I t gives us lots of energy
T o do many things
S uch as playing and learning in school.

Sofia Visheva (6)
Hazelwood Schools, Palmers Green

My Family

I love my family,
My family loves me,
Together forever, we will always be.
My sister is funny, she is the best.
She is better than all the rest!
My dad is strong, he is so tall,
He gives the biggest hugs of all.
I love my mum and she loves me,
Together we are a happy family.

Alana Scarlett Lambrou (7)
Hazelwood Schools, Palmers Green

Spider-Man

S pidey sense is tingling.
P eter Parker has spider powers.
I s he strong?
D efinitely.
E veryone likes him
R ed and blue costume.
 -
M J is his friend.
A unt May is his family.
N o one can beat him.

Jack Bufton (5)
Hazelwood Schools, Palmers Green

Seasons

S pring rain pitter-patters in my garden.
E verything comes to life after wintertime.
A ll the flowers bloom when the
S un shines brightly, warm and burning.
O ranges and pineapples will be ready in the autumn.
N ature is good in every season.

Nell Naughton (6)
Hazelwood Schools, Palmers Green

Trains And Drivers

T rains rush fast on the tracks.
R un fast like a tube train.
A s the train stops, the people get on the trains.
I nside the trains, there are seats for people to sit.
N o one can drive better than train drivers.
S team is made out of water.

Matthew Kalemi (7)
Hazelwood Schools, Palmers Green

Football

F ind a field to play on
O n a sunny day.
O nto the goal, smashing the big net.
T ackle the other team to win the ball
B ut make sure your goalie is good
A nd try to win the game.
L ots of luck.
L ots of great goals.

Luca Antoniades (6)
Hazelwood Schools, Palmers Green

Superman

S uperpowers scare villains away.
U p, up and away
P owerfully he saved the town
E normous super speed
R ocket from another planet
M r Kent came from space
A nother of his powers is flying
N o one is as strong as him

Wiktor Swietochowski (6)
Hazelwood Schools, Palmers Green

Fairy

F ast and delicate, my angel with magical wings.
A lways tiny, she loves playing hide-and-seek with me.
I ts tiny wings, shimmering like magic.
R acing ahead, spreading sparkly dust in its path.
Y es, gold glitter, a fairy dust trail for me to find.

Aashna Pankhania (6)
Hazelwood Schools, Palmers Green

Rabbits

R unning, jumping, hopping faster than a mouse.
A carrot keeps my long teeth sharp.
B urrows are a place I live in.
B ringing you Easter eggs every year.
I can hear from far and near with my long ears.
T ake my foot for good luck.

Emma Serafinova-Noel (6)
Hazelwood Schools, Palmers Green

Plants

I love plants and seeds,
They are fantastic indeed.

I put a seed in the soil
But my baby sister made it spoil.

I tried again in another pot,
Keeping it away from the baby's cot.

Roots grow under the ground,
Plants can feel everything around.

Marawan Elawadi (6)
Hazelwood Schools, Palmers Green

My School Life

S o many new things to learn.
C lubs to teach me football and chess.
H elp when I need it to be my best.
O n Tuesday, I get to play until late.
O ver the last year, I have changed so much.
L ovely school, so much more to do.

Alex Rawlinson (6)
Hazelwood Schools, Palmers Green

My Cat, Hedgehog, Can Fly!

Hedgehogs like muddy puddles.
My cat, Hedgehog, can fly.
Hedgehog feels like a fuzzy blanket.
My cat, Hedgehog, can fly.
Hedgehog looks like a dusty rug.
My cat, Hedgehog, can fly.
Hedgehog sounds like a squeaking weasel.
My cat, Hedgehog, can fly.

Joe Robertson (7)
Hazelwood Schools, Palmers Green

What Animal Am I?

I only purr, I never roar.
I have four legs that each have a paw.
I am a well-known type of cat.
My teeth are sharp, so do not pat.
My name is also a type of car.
I have black spots and can run far.
What am I?

Answer: A jaguar.

Edgar Loustalan (6)
Hazelwood Schools, Palmers Green

Chelsea

C helsea is the winning team.
H azard is their captain.
E uropa final is their dream.
L onging for a special win.
S inging is what we will do.
E very time we win against you
A nd we will sing again.

Emma Sales (7)
Hazelwood Schools, Palmers Green

Me And My Bicycle

Today it is May.
Birds tweet in a beautiful way.
Fresh air is blowing and flowing.
Tyres on my bicycle are rolling.
There is sunshine on my face.
There are bugs on my shoelace.
I like the day that it is today,
Because it's a beautiful day in May.

Balazs Csanadi (7)
Hazelwood Schools, Palmers Green

Dancing

D ancing is fun!
A lot of exciting music.
N ever stop, keep on moving.
C ome dancing with me.
I 'm fantastic at ballet and tap.
N othing is as brilliant as music.
G et up and start moving.

Stella Frangou (6)
Hazelwood Schools, Palmers Green

Rabbits

R ichard was a rabbit.
A lone he lived.
B y himself in a woody habitat.
B urrowed deep.
I nside, he had a terrible habit.
T hank goodness he had a wonderful cabbage tree to keep him company.

Arabella Procter (5)
Hazelwood Schools, Palmers Green

Dragons

D ragons are scary.
R ed dragons are on fire.
A ren't they terrifying?
G o dragons, go!
O h no, the dragons are coming.
N ow they are really angry.
S ome more dragons come!

Sachin Verma (6)
Hazelwood Schools, Palmers Green

Nice And Warm Riddle

I have a zip.
I am longer than a person.
I am nice, snuggly and warm.
You sleep inside me.
You roll me up inside of a bag when you are not using me.
You use me for camping.
What am I?

Answer: A sleeping bag.

Indie Houghton (6)
Hazelwood Schools, Palmers Green

Lions

L ook who is hiding in the high grass.
I n the endless African savannah.
O MG, the rhinos are not afraid of them,
N ever play with them, they aren't a pussy cat.
S ome of them live in a zoo.

Alisa Yushchuk (6)
Hazelwood Schools, Palmers Green

The Useful Engine

I am blue, red and black.
I am running every day faster and faster.
I have the number one on me.
I eat all my coal.
I am a very useful and good engine.
Who am I?

Answer: I am Thomas the Tank Engine.

Panagiotis Tselios (7)
Hazelwood Schools, Palmers Green

My Favourite Bird

F eathers are pink.
L ong skinny legs.
A lways looking for food.
M y favourite bird
I s the flamingo
N ice and friendly
G reat to see
O h so pink and lovely.

Selen Eyyub (6)
Hazelwood Schools, Palmers Green

Let The Game Start

I play loads of games.
Everybody aims.
I get loads of wins
Most people hide in bins.
I go to Tilted Towers
To use my powers.
I buy loads of skins
Hope they come with wings.
My name is Kevin
And I love to sleep in.

Kevin Hukalowicz (6)
Hazelwood Schools, Palmers Green

Summer

Summer looks like the sun glowing.
Summer sounds like boats rowing.
Summer feels dry like sand.
Summer smells like sun cream on your hand.
Summer tastes like strawberry granita,
Add some sugar and it'll taste even sweeter.

Alessio Vento-Joyce (7)
Hazelwood Schools, Palmers Green

I Love Swimming

S un is hot.
W hy can't I go swimming?
I t is fun.
M aking splashes.
M um comes in as well.
I play catching.
N ow I am a dolphin.
G reat, I love it.

Rosie Thwaites (6)
Hazelwood Schools, Palmers Green

Summer

Summer looks like flowers blooming.
Summer sounds like bees zooming.
Summer tastes like cold drinks fizzing.
Summer smells like BBQs sizzling.
Summer feels like warm sun on my skin.
I can't wait for summer to begin!

Lucas Morris (7)
Hazelwood Schools, Palmers Green

The Best Game Ever!

It is always round.
It is part of a game.
It can be in many different colours.
It is bouncy.
You can kick it high and far.
You can kick it into a goal.
What am I?

Answer: A football.

Ben Gibbard (6)
Hazelwood Schools, Palmers Green

Winter

W inter is as cold as the Antarctic.
I n winter you have to wear a coat.
N o, winter is not hot.
T ake care of yourself.
E nd of winter is summer.
R elax and be happy.

Ahmet Tuncel (7)
Hazelwood Schools, Palmers Green

My Flower

I had a little seed
And I put it in a pot.
I put it in the sunshine
And I watered it a lot.

I waited and waited,
I watched it grow and grow.
Then one day a flower
Came out to say hello.

Spyros Gkezos (7)
Hazelwood Schools, Palmers Green

A Prince's Life

The prince looks handsome and smart.
He feels proud about his art.
His piano playing sounds cool with a beat.
The prince smells lovely and sweet.
He was served some tasty dates,
A prince's life is great!

Rosa Beana Watson (7)
Hazelwood Schools, Palmers Green

The Time That The Monsters Came

M onsters are scary
O h my goodness
N ever come near us
S hock, horror!
T urn and run away,
E at them up!
R oast them,
S hout the ugly monsters.

Barney Hailstone (6)
Hazelwood Schools, Palmers Green

Brilliant Fruit

F abulous as ice cream.
R inse your apples to taste brand new.
U nder the ground, seeds will sprout.
I n the trees, apples grow.
T he lemons are sour and your eyes water.

Alexander Philippos Costa Enright (6)
Hazelwood Schools, Palmers Green

Animals And Pets

I lift my ears when I hear a noise.
I wear a furry, grey coat.
I eat yummy food.
I live in a nice warm home.
I live with an owner called Sophia.
What am I?

Answer: Chopper, the pet.

Sophia Velez Moncada (7)
Hazelwood Schools, Palmers Green

Kings Go Wrong In My Dream

It was a sunny afternoon,
Where there was no moon
I was playing 'Kings' with my friends
And in the corner of my eye,
I could see my sister...
Whoosh! We got sucked into the game.

Angelo Odunoye (6)
Hazelwood Schools, Palmers Green

Stars

S tars are bright.
T winkle and sparkle in the sky.
A shooting star fell from the sky.
R adiant like a diamond.
S taring at the stars in the sky makes me feel good.

Chloe Philipou (6)
Hazelwood Schools, Palmers Green

Dragon Night

Dragon Night is very strong
He has wings and superpowers
He can fly and breathe fires
When the danger came into the world
Dragon Night is on his way
Here he comes, to save the day.

Ilirdi Bregu (6)
Hazelwood Schools, Palmers Green

A Summer's Day

Summer days look bright and shiny.
Summer daisies look so tiny.
The air smells so clean and warm.
I can see the white clouds form.
Summer rainbows are so clear,
I love summer, it's so near!

Jessica Kyriacou (7)
Hazelwood Schools, Palmers Green

Puppies

P uppies
U seful puppies
P layful puppies
P ut things in their mouths
I ncredible puppies
E nergetic puppies
S leepy puppies.

Lillian Ewan (6)
Hazelwood Schools, Palmers Green

Bunny

B ouncy bunny is so funny.
U nder the sheets in my bed.
N ever bad, always good.
N ever go away, stay with me,
Y ou love me, my fluffy pink friend.

Leah Andrews (5)
Hazelwood Schools, Palmers Green

Who Am I?

I have a golden crown.
I wear a long velvet dress.
People call me 'Your Majesty'.
My son is called Prince Charles.
Who am I?

Answer: Queen Elizabeth II.

Emma Kyriacou (7)
Hazelwood Schools, Palmers Green

Riddle Of The Deep Blue Sea

I am beautiful and very colourful.
I am half fish and half person.
I have a lot of sea creatures as friends.
I am a good swimmer.
What am I?

Answer: A mermaid.

Autumn Wallis Ackroyd (7)
Hazelwood Schools, Palmers Green

Going To The Cinema

C ome and see a film.
I saw Detective Pikachu.
N ew ones every week.
E ating sweets.
M ovies are sometimes scary.
A lways amazing.

Arthur Gatland (6)
Hazelwood Schools, Palmers Green

Winter Wonderland

W inter is stormy.
I play in the snow.
N ow it is winter,
T he north wind will blow.
E veryone is cold,
R iding sleighs, ho, ho!

Annabelle El Issa (6)
Hazelwood Schools, Palmers Green

Autumn

Autumn feels cosy.
Autumn tastes like a cold radiator.
Autumn smells like Bonfire Night.
Autumn sounds like feet stomping.
Autumn looks orange, brown and golden.

Uthmaan Khairul (6)
Hazelwood Schools, Palmers Green

Toys

I like toys because when I play with them, it makes me happy.
I like toys because some toys are big and some are small.
I like toys because they come in different shapes.

Aynur Kara (7)
Hazelwood Schools, Palmers Green

Rabbit

R abbits are cute.
A lways jumping.
B eautifully pink.
B unny is my name.
I t is my favourite.
T iny and fluffy.

Maya Feier (6)
Hazelwood Schools, Palmers Green

Tasty Me

I am as white as Santa Claus' beard.
I am as cold as the North Pole.
I can be as colourful as a rainbow.
I can be melted when I'm hot.
What am I?

Sara Xhafa (6)
Hazelwood Schools, Palmers Green

Guess Me!

I like to be funny.
I am as cheeky as a monkey.
I can sometimes be greedy and lazy.
I am very playful.
What am I?

Answer: A kitten.

Pandora Paola Dimou (6)
Hazelwood Schools, Palmers Green

What Am I?

I fly across the world.
I have wings and a tail.
I make a noise.
I fly above clouds as white as snow.
What am I?

Answer: A plane.

Aaron Andrews (7)
Hazelwood Schools, Palmers Green

Healthy Food

F ruit is healthy for you.
R ed fruits are yummy.
U p in the trees.
I like pineapple.
T he grapes are tasty.

Sylvie Chambers (6)
Hazelwood Schools, Palmers Green

PAW Patrol

H eadquarters is where they meet.
E ating time is at 12pm
R escuing is their game
O ranges are their rewards.

Aryaan Hussain (5)
Hazelwood Schools, Palmers Green

The Shining Star

S hining bright in the sky
U ntil the day goes by
N ight-time it sleeps whilst its brother, the moon, gleams.

Zayah Szabo Alexander (5)
Hazelwood Schools, Palmers Green

The World

Animals are friendly.
The world is our home,
Let's treat it nicely and with care.
So we can share it with everyone.

Skyla Deegan (6)
Hazelwood Schools, Palmers Green

Cats

C ats are cute.
A cat is cuddly.
T riangular ears.
S nuggly pets to have.

Astrid Mosquera (6)
Hazelwood Schools, Palmers Green

Time For School

Time for school, so here I come!
Hello teacher, bye-bye Mum.
Hello friends, another day,
Hours and hours to work and play.
Books to read and sums to do,
Stories, paintings, pictures too.
When the bell rings, we go out.
Run around, laugh and shout.
Then back in through the classroom door,
We're quiet again, we work some more.
We sing, we clap, we stomp our feet,
And then, at last, it's time to eat.
More play, more work, all afternoon,
I'm tired, is it home time soon?
Half-past three, home time has come,
Bye-bye teacher, hello Mum.

Levi Avram (6)
Kingsbury Green Primary School, Kingsbury

Winter

Winter is white and as quiet as can be,
The branches are bare on the maple tree.
Winter brings snow falling all around,
Animals are sleeping quietly underground.
Nights are so long and the days are so short,
Time to go skiing, my favourite winter sport.
Winter brings snowstorms, snow blowing everywhere,
Temperatures are freezing, warm clothes I will wear.
Winter brings hot cocoa with marshmallows too,
Winter is here, we welcome you.
Winter spreads in the white sheet,
It is time to greet winter with some woollen clothes.

Manit Prashant Patel (7)
Kingsbury Green Primary School, Kingsbury

Walking To School On A Rainy Day

To the beat of the rain,
The trees dance and sway,
The rain seeps down
My raincoat neck, dripping, dripping,
Every which way.
I smell the earth all soggy and wet.
A boom, a flash! I scurry along
And slip and trip but then I stop
And enjoy each drop.
I taste a raindrop on my cheek,
It's salty and it's kind of sweet.
I let myself get wonderfully wet
And jump into the next big puddle.

Ahmed Omran Istanakzai (7)
Kingsbury Green Primary School, Kingsbury

Big Baking

B ig baking is fun and great.
I love making cupcakes on my plate!
G reat cakes from ideas that I create.

B utter, chocolate, flour and strawberries are all the ingredients I need.
A pple pie is very delicious.
K eeping clean is very hard to do.
I love the tasty icing.
N om, nom! The sprinkles are yummy.
G etting messy is the best part of the fun!

Rochelle Minara Wimalasuriya (7)
Kingsbury Green Primary School, Kingsbury

Cricket

C alculating times tables becomes fun.
R acing to save the ball from the boundary.
I enjoy the game because it keeps me fit.
C atching the ball when it comes to me in the air.
K eeps me active almost the whole day.
E nergetic I become if I play cricket.
T eaches me to learn spirit and teamwork.

Dhruv Sompura (6)
Kingsbury Green Primary School, Kingsbury

Over The Rainbows

R ainbows are big, colourful things.
A ll these colours come from a rainbow.
I ndigo, purple, green, blue and pink.
N ow there is a rainbow in front of me.
B ees are flying in-between the colours and having fun.
O ver the rainbow, the butterflies went.
W hen I see a rainbow, I feel happy.

Gino Brian (7)
Kingsbury Green Primary School, Kingsbury

Summer's Already Here!

Chirping birds fly,
In the clear blue sky.
I can't believe it!
Summer's already here!

Flies buzzing around,
Ice cream van sounds.
It's so clear!
Summer's already here!

Sweat trickling down,
Lazing on the lawn.
No more waiting,
For summer's already here!

Ayaan Chaudhary (7)
Kingsbury Green Primary School, Kingsbury

Creatures For Life

U nique magical creatures.
N ice rainbow hair on their backs.
I ce powers that they have.
C andy is their thing.
O nions they don't like.
R unning fast from their enemies.
N ew baby creatures are the best.

Elizabeth Triboi (6)
Kingsbury Green Primary School, Kingsbury

The Tired Tiger

T rying to catch animals and have them as my prey.
I get tired of chasing them all day.
G rowling at them and pouncing.
E ating gives me energy from up and all around.
R unning everywhere all day is harder than you expect.

Zainab Bader (6)
Kingsbury Green Primary School, Kingsbury

Nature

Nature looks like a thousand different colours.
Nature sounds like rustling leaves on a windy day.
Nature feels like the warmth of the sun on my skin.
Nature tastes like freshly picked blackberries.
Nature smells like a garden full of beautiful flowers.

Mikael Alderton (6)
Kingsbury Green Primary School, Kingsbury

Farmer

F armer is what I want to be.
A pples that I want to grow myself.
M y family to eat healthy because
I want them to live forever.
L ove is what I feel.
Y eah, I love my family.

David Boca (7)
Kingsbury Green Primary School, Kingsbury

The Panda Poem

P laying in the jungle.
A nd playing with other pandas.
N ot annoying anyone and being nice.
D ad and Mum love me so they give me a present.
A few colours I have are black and white.

Hussain Ali-Mostafa (7)
Kingsbury Green Primary School, Kingsbury

Summer

Summer is good for fun in the sun.
Summer smells of mowed grass.
Summer tastes like roast dinner.
Summer feels easy like my bed.
Summer reminds me of Bonfire Night.
Summer sounds quiet as animals sleep.

Eduard Reut (7)
Kingsbury Green Primary School, Kingsbury

Four Seasons

There are four seasons
That never change.
Winter brings the snow,
Spring brings the flowers,
Summer brings hotness,
Autumn brings darkness.

Dihen Fernando (6)
Kingsbury Green Primary School, Kingsbury

Today Is A Winter Day

Winter is like Christmas.
Winter people sing and sledge.
Winter has snow.
Winter is cold.
Winter is not hot, it is very cold.

Preesha Rabadia (6)
Kingsbury Green Primary School, Kingsbury

Summer

The sound of the lovely children playing in the blazing hot sun.
The sound of the BBC news up in that gigantic skyscraper towering above me.
The smell of my mum and dad making a secret barbecue in my garden.
The smell of the radical sea water splashing on me.
The taste of the delicious white Magnum resting in my mouth.
The taste of some yummy pie and whipped cream.
The sight of the epic sun rising.
The sight of a Lamborghini racing in front of me,
Makes me feel excited.

Laith Alexander Brookman-Amissah (7)
St Luke's CE School, London

Winter

The sound of children playing in the snow.
The smell of warm yummy food cooking in the oven.
The taste of cold snow.
The feeling of crunchy snow under my feet.
The sight of sensible children playing, skiing and ice skating,
Makes me want to dance and sing.

Zoey Hoffmann (5)
St Luke's CE School, London

Autumn

The sound of golden leaves crunching under my feet.
The smell of yummy fresh soup.
The taste of super, good Halloween sweets.
The feel of the frosty air around me.
The sight of trick-or-treaters collecting candy, makes me feel happy inside.

Abigail Hoffmann (7)
St Luke's CE School, London

Summer

The sound of pretty birds singing...
The smell of chocolate ice cream...
The taste of a cool fruit smoothie...
The feel of the big green leaves...
The sight of the beautiful flowers...
...Makes me want to dance!

Pardis Ashouri (7)
St Luke's CE School, London

Winter

The sound of children playing in the snow.
The smell of my mum's delicious shepherd's pie.
The taste of hot chocolate.
The feel of the warmth in my bed.
The sight of my family,
Makes me feel very happy.

Chara Bewsher (6)
St Luke's CE School, London

Winter

The sound of snow crunching when I step on it.
The smell of fish and chips.
The taste of spaghetti.
The feel of crunchy snow in my hands.
The sight of children playing in the snow,
Makes me play in the snow too.

Aidegueosa Eliana Adun (6)
St Luke's CE School, London

Summer

The sound of the blue waves splashing.
The smell of yummy chocolate ice-cream.
The taste of rainbow ice lollies.
The feel of the soft, green grass.
The sight of beautiful butterflies.
...Makes me love summertime.

Partow Ashouri (7)
St Luke's CE School, London

Summer

The sound of beautiful birds chirping.
The smell of honey from the bees.
The taste of delicious ice cream.
The feel of cushions under my head.
The sight of adorable kittens,
Makes me dance and sing.

Haruna Miura (5)
St Luke's CE School, London

Winter

Winter sounds like everyone singing happily in a white tree.
The smell of my mum's hot dishes,
my mum's spaghetti slurping.
The feel of the cold wind under my toes making me laugh and smile.

Tamia Burrell (6)
St Luke's CE School, London

Spring

The sound of beautiful birds singing,
The smell of the nice, fragrant flowers,
The taste of hot chocolate,
The feel of the soft grass,
The sight of children playing,
Makes me want it to be spring already.

Mikey Chatterton (7)
St Luke's CE School, London

Summer

The sound of birds chirping on trees.
The smell of fresh candyfloss.
The taste of strawberry ice cream.
The feel of my cosy coat.
The sight of lovely pink flowers,
Makes me giggle and dance.

Marcus Meduri (6)
St Luke's CE School, London

Spring

The sound of birds singing.
The smell of fresh flowers.
The taste of sweet honey from the bees.
The feel of white, fluffy bunnies.
The sight of children playing with flowers,
Makes me dance happily.

Zeinab Haider (7)
St Luke's CE School, London

Spring

The sound of sweet birds chirping.
The smell of fresh flowers.
The taste of buzzing bees' honey.
The feel of smooth birds' eggs.
The sight of adorable chicks,
Makes me shout and sing.

Isambard Geers (6)
St Luke's CE School, London

Summer

The sound of the summer wind blowing.
The smell of the freshly chopped grass.
The taste of a delicious meal in the sun.
The feel of the sun shining bright.
The sight makes me giggle and wriggle.

Sofia Phillips (6)
St Luke's CE School, London

Spring

The sound of sweet birds singing.
The smell of flowers in trees.
The taste of my mum's food in the oven.
The feel of soft cats.
The sight of lovely animals,
Makes me clap and jump.

Elle Jay Marshall (7)
St Luke's CE School, London

Summer

The sound of children playing in the park.
The smell of fresh honey sandwiches.
The taste of delicious doughnuts.
The feel of the hot sun on my skin,
Makes me want to shout and sing.

Olivia McKenzie (6)
St Luke's CE School, London

Winter

The sound of crunchy snow in my hands.
The smell of marshmallows.
The taste of hot chocolate.
The feel of falling snow.
The sight of Christmas presents,
Make me dance happily.

Claudia Kordys (7)
St Luke's CE School, London

Summer

The sound of children playing.
The smell of pretty flowers.
The taste of ice cream.
The feel of the sun shining on me.
The sight of the green grass,
Makes me jump with joy.

Rachel Blach de Faoite (6) & Lara
St Luke's CE School, London

Spring

The sound of the rain dropping on my house.
The smell of my delicious, fresh salad.
The feel of the rain dropping on my hat.
The sight of birdies tweeting makes me feel happy.

Rose Orly Raftery (5)
St Luke's CE School, London

Spring

The sound of birds chirping.
The smell of fresh flowers.
The taste of a sandwich.
The feel of soft grass.
The sight of birds singing,
Makes me shout and sing.

Matian Bllaca (7)
St Luke's CE School, London

Summer

The sound of waves.
The smell of ice lollies.
The taste of my dinner.
The feel of the hot sun.
The sight of children playing,
It all makes me dance and sing.

Georgina Gross (6)
St Luke's CE School, London

Summer

The sound of the crunchy leaves.
The smell of the green blowing grass.
The taste of freezing ice cream.
The feel of the soft trees.
The sight of the hot sun.

Aaron Predko (6)
St Luke's CE School, London

Summer

The sound of birds chirping.
The smell of fresh honey.
The taste of new lollies.
The feel of cold water.
The sight of children laughing,
Makes me sing.

Beck Talanbek (5)
St Luke's CE School, London

Summer

The sound of children playing,
The smell of pretty flowers
The taste of ice cream.
The feel of sand.

Michael Kudi Mafuamba (6)
St Luke's CE School, London

The Seasons

S easons like a long day of fun.
E nd of autumn and winter makes it more fun for you.
A nd you can have some relaxing time in spring and summer.
S ome of that is play as well because everyone likes playing.
O f course, everyone loves it because it's like a day out.
N ot winter or autumn but summer and spring are the best.
S o if you like the seasons, we're in them and the one we're in now is summer.

Dara Olowoporoku (7)
St Mark's CE Primary School, Islington

The Mermaid

M ermaids have beautiful hair like a teacher.
E very mermaid has a pretty tail.
R eal mermaids normally go down to the bottom.
M ost mermaids are usually bored in the sea.
A mermaid is really good at singing.
I t is also good at swimming underwater.
D id you know that mermaids can be boys?

Savannah Emily de Barry (7)
St Mark's CE Primary School, Islington

The Best Malik At Football

F un and rewarding with a certificate and a medal.
O utside playing football.
O ur team win the match.
T racking back when the other team has the ball.
B eing a team player.
A lways scoring goals.
L ots of fun because everyone is passing to me.
L ove to play football.

Malik Adam (7)
St Mark's CE Primary School, Islington

Animals

K ittens have fur that feels like a cloud.
I ncredibly sharp claws like a knife.
T wo or one baby cats that are so cute.
T oo adorable, just like a button.
E yes sparkle like the stars.
N ice and protected.
S leepy kittens after a long day.

Nomqhele Zoleka Khumalo (7)
St Mark's CE Primary School, Islington

The Amazing!

I am floaty.
I am a piece of clothing.
I am frilly and girls wear me.
People like to wear me in the summer.
I live in a cupboard.
I haven't got arms or legs.
What am I?

Answer: A dress.

Romola Hume-Wright (6)
St Mark's CE Primary School, Islington

Rabbits

R abbits eat radishes.
A lways like a playful puppy.
B rave like a spy.
B ig ears like the Bible.
I mpressive high jumps.
T alented teeth.
S uper fast like a car.

Cerys Rose Miller (6)
St Mark's CE Primary School, Islington

The Hot Summer

S unny at the beach.
U mbrella for the shade.
M en can go to the beach.
M um can go to the swimming pool.
E very day the sun comes out.
R eally love the beach.

Rayanne Kasongo (7)
St Mark's CE Primary School, Islington

About Lions

L icking an ice cream in the back garden.
I mpressive lions from the zoo.
O ne lion has entered the zoo.
N ew lions entered our house.
S leeping lions are in the garden.

Kamran Salik (7)
St Mark's CE Primary School, Islington

Rabbit

R abbits can jump as high as the BFG.
A rabbit has long ears.
B unnies bounce around.
B eautiful bunnies.
I nside rabbits eat a lot.
T iny rabbits.

Jacob Sipiano (6)
St Mark's CE Primary School, Islington

Super

D erek is my best friend as a king.
E dmund is as fast as everyone.
R ocking, roles like a monkey.
E lephants are as strong as rhinos.
K ing over everything.

Deniz Dogan (7)
St Mark's CE Primary School, Islington

Fast Runner

I am a really fast runner.
I have four legs and I am orange with black spots.
I have sharp teeth.
I have sharp claws.
I am an animal.
What am I?

Answer: A cheetah.

Jeriel Annan (5)
St Mark's CE Primary School, Islington

Invisible Water

I am invisible, I come from the sky.
I am wet and people wear hoods.
People drink me.
I make flowers grow.
I live in the sky.
What am I?

Answer: The rain

Pelumi Olujinmi (6)
St Mark's CE Primary School, Islington

The Grey Animal

I am grey, fast and nifty.
I live on all continents.
I live in New York and England and in trees.
I am a predator.
I eat pigeons for breakfast, lunch and dinner.
What am I?

Zackariah Ashik-O'Toole (6)
St Mark's CE Primary School, Islington

Colourful Thing

I am lots of colours and very beautiful.
I live in the sky.
You can only see me when there is sun and rain together.
What am I?

Answer: A rainbow.

Joshua Falanka (6)
St Mark's CE Primary School, Islington

The Magical Creature

I have white and pink hair.
I live in the forest.
I am magical.
I live in the sky.
I have so much colour.
What am I?

Answer: A unicorn.

Jianing Guo (6)
St Mark's CE Primary School, Islington

Sea Life

I have fins and scales.
I have blue eyes.
I live in the sea.
I see dolphins.
I have arms.
I can talk.
Who could I be?

Answer: A mermaid.

Bayleigh Sweeney (6)
St Mark's CE Primary School, Islington

In The City!

I am black.
I live outside on the pavements.
Vehicles drive on me.
You cross on me.
I am very long.
What am I?

Answer: A road.

Asa Morphet (6)
St Mark's CE Primary School, Islington

Animals

My cat is like a bird.
My bird is like an ant.
My chick is like a mouse.
My mouse is like a clown.
My tiger is like an elephant.
My bear is like a polar bear.

Maisarah Miah (7)
St Mark's CE Primary School, Islington

Blue Earth

I love surfboards on top of me.
I have seaweed in me.
I am wet.
I live all over the world.
What am I?

Answer: *The ocean.*

Xanti Leizaola (6)
St Mark's CE Primary School, Islington

The Slow Animal

I am slimy and black.
I am below the ground.
I am slowly eating leaves.
I live in the leaves.
What am I?

Answer: A slug.

Ava Cunningham (6)
St Mark's CE Primary School, Islington

The Fierce Predator

I am strong and fierce.
I have sharp claws.
I have sharp teeth.
I have big, long brown hair.
What am I?

Answer: A lion.

Jimmy Pipinka (6)
St Mark's CE Primary School, Islington

Royal Boss

I am important.
I live in a place.
I am bossy.
I am rich.
I am naughty.
I am cool.
What am I?

Answer: A queen.

Nylah Dirosa-Brown (6)
St Mark's CE Primary School, Islington

The Pink Animal

I am pink.
I have sounds.
I live on a farm.
I keep my piglets safe.
What am I?

Answer: A pig.

Christian Solarin (6)
St Mark's CE Primary School, Islington

The Royal Palace

I am a very big building.
I live in London.
The Queen lives inside.
What am I?

Answer: Buckingham Palace.

Rufus Morrell (6)
St Mark's CE Primary School, Islington

Cat

C limb as fast as lightning.
A lways eating as fast as the night's hot wind.
T earing furniture.

Dimitris Zamenopoulos (7)
St Mark's CE Primary School, Islington

Important Person

I am important.
I have a crown.
I have servants to protect me.
What am I?

Answer: A king.

Ethan Matthews-Appleby (6)
St Mark's CE Primary School, Islington

Black Animal

I am black and tiny.
I live in the leaves.
I am strong.
What am I?

Answer: An ant.

Daniel Adkin (6)
St Mark's CE Primary School, Islington

Super Red

I am red and orange.
I am strong.
I am beautiful.
What am I?

Answer: A phoenix.

J'Quan Jackman (6)
St Mark's CE Primary School, Islington

Cave Animal

I am brown.
I am big.
I am furry.
I live in a cave.
What am I?

Answer: A bear.

Arjol William Xhihaj (6)
St Mark's CE Primary School, Islington

A Bright Circle

I am shiny and hot.
I live in the sky.
I am powerful.
What am I?

Answer: The sun.

Sadie Taitt (6)
St Mark's CE Primary School, Islington

Young Writers Information

We hope you have enjoyed reading this book – and that you will continue to in the coming years.

If you're a young writer who enjoys reading and creative writing, or the parent of an enthusiastic poet or story writer, do visit our website **www.youngwriters.co.uk**. Here you will find free competitions, workshops and games, as well as recommended reads, a poetry glossary and our blog.

If you would like to order further copies of this book, or any of our other titles, then please give us a call or visit **www.youngwriters.co.uk**.

Young Writers
Remus House
Coltsfoot Drive
Peterborough
PE2 9BF
(01733) 890066
info@youngwriters.co.uk

@YoungWritersUK   @YoungWritersCW